This edition published by Parragon Books Ltd in 2015

Parragon Books Ltd
Chartist House
15–17 Trim Street
Bath BA1 1HA, UK
www.parragon.com

ISBN 978-1-4723-9602-0

Printed in China

From the movie
Disney
FROZEN

Olaf's Fun File

PaRragon
Bath • New York • Cologne • Melbourne • Delhi
Hong Kong • Shenzhen • Singapore • Amsterdam

This book
belongs to

_____

Summer had finally arrived in Arendelle
and everyone in the kingdom was enjoying
the long, sunny days after a very cold
winter season.

Today was going to be the hottest day
of the year so far! Most of the villagers
wanted to stay inside where it was cool.

Olaf, on the other hand, could hardly wait to get outside. This was the kind of day he had always dreamed about!

Olaf ran into Princess Anna's room, calling out happily.

"Anna, Anna! Guess what today is? It's the perfect summery day! Let's go outside and play!"

Anna groaned as she sat up in bed. "It's so hot and sticky, Olaf." But she had to smile when she saw Olaf's hopeful face.

Together, Olaf and Anna went to look for Queen Elsa.
They found her in the Great Hall, talking with a visitor.

"Please, can we go play in the sunshine?" Olaf asked Elsa.

Elsa laughed. "That sounds like fun, Olaf!"

"It's so hot, though," Anna said. "Couldn't you cool things
down just a bit, Elsa?"

"Olaf has always wanted to experience a hot summer's day," said Elsa. "Shouldn't we give him his wish? We'll do everything he's always wanted to do in summer!"

"You're right, Elsa," agreed Anna. "How about a picnic on the shores of the fjord?"

Olaf clasped his hands with glee. "Oooh, I love picnics!"

As soon as the trio stepped outside, Anna felt so hot that she plopped straight down on to the grass. Olaf began chasing a bumblebee.

"Come along," said Elsa. "Let's head to the docks – we can sail to the perfect picnic spot."

Olaf stopped in his tracks. "We're going sailing? I've always wanted to try sailing!"

At the docks, Anna and Elsa chose a beautiful sailing boat.
As they set sail, Olaf hummed happily. He even got to steer!

When they reached the shore, Elsa set up the picnic. But Olaf couldn't sit still.

"Don't you just love the feeling of sand on your snow?" he squealed. "Let's make sand angels!"

Anna gingerly stuck a toe in the hot sand. "Oh, goodness, that is … warm!" she squeaked.

Anna tiptoed over to the fjord's edge. "Ah, this is better," she said, as water washed over her feet.

The three friends spent the whole afternoon playing in the summer sun.

They built sand castles and sand people.

They chased waves on the shore
and even danced with seagulls.

And finally, when they had tired themselves out,
Anna, Elsa and Olaf had their picnic on the shore.
"Hands down, this is the best day of my life," said Olaf.

Later, as they sailed back to Arendelle, the setting sun made beautiful colours in the sky. Olaf was amazed. "I wish I could hug the summer sun. I bet it would feel wonderful!"

Anna smiled as she swept her sweaty hair off her face. "You might need a bigger snow cloud for that, Olaf."

Back at the docks, Kristoff and Sven were waiting.
They had spent the afternoon harvesting ice. Anna jumped
out of the boat and flung herself on the cold blocks.

"Oh am I glad to see you!" she cried.

Olaf told Kristoff and Sven all about their adventures.

"I wish it could always be summer!" Olaf said.

"Summer is wonderful," Elsa agreed, smiling. But secretly
she had had enough of the boiling weather.

"Tomorrow," she said with a wink, "I predict snow."

ALL ABOUT ME

Olaf wants to know everything about you!
Fill in these pages.

Name ....

Age ....

Birthday ....

Eye colour ....

Shoe size ....

Hair colour ....

Best friends ....

....

....

....

Best talent ....

....

Worst habit ....

....

Happiest moment ....

....

....

....

FUN PHOTOS

Glue in some photographs of you having fun!

Olaf and Sven

FRIENDS WORTH MELTING FOR

Olaf thinks his friends are the best in the whole world!

Name **Elsa**

Why she's worth melting for

She made me! And she did a good job, if I do say so myself.

Best thing she's done for me

Gave me my own snow flurry, so I wouldn't melt in the warm weather.

Name **Anna**

Why she's worth melting for

She is brave and always looks on the bright side, like I do!

Best thing she's done for me

She always puts me back together when my body's all over the place.

Name **Kristoff**

Why he's worth melting for
> He looks after Anna and stops
> Sven from eating my nose!

Best thing he's done for me
> He saved my snow a few times
> on our adventure in the mountains.

Name **Sven**

Why he's worth melting for
> He's a big, cuddly reindeer!
> What's not to love?

Best thing he's done for me
> Not eaten my carrot nose.

MY ICE-COOL FRIENDS

Now fill in the details of your own best friends.

Name ....

Why he/she is worth melting for ....

....

Best thing he/she has done for me ....

....

....

Name ....

Why he/she is worth melting for ....

....

Best thing he/she has done for me ....

....

....

Name ....

Why he/she is worth melting for ....

....

Best thing he/she has done for me ....

....

....

Name ....

Why he/she is worth melting for ....

....

Best thing he/she has done for me ....

....

FRIENDSHIP PHOTOS

Glue in some photographs of you and your friends having a fun time!

Best friends

FAVUURITE THINGS

Write your favourite thing that you think of for each of the items below.

Season

ANIMAL

FRIEND

Colour

Book

NUMBER

SNOWY SECRETS

Tell Olaf your biggest secrets! He's a good friend and will keep them safe.

Something I've never told anyone

....

....

....

Something I've only told my best friend

....

....

....

My biggest secret wish ....
....

Something I secretly think is really fun

....

....

Secretly my favourite person in the world

....

....

OLAF LOVES SUMMER!

Ever wondered why this snowman dreams of summer?
Check out his reasons below.

Sunshine

I love the feel of the sun on my face!

FLOWERS

I love the look and smell of summer flowers.
I don't get to see them in the winter!

The beach

Lying on the sand with an ice-cool drink
in my hand would be my perfect day.

HEAT

I can't help it – I love heat!

Which is your favourite season and why?

My favourite season is ....

Here are my reasons

1. ....

2. ....

3. ....

4. ....

JUST IMAGINE...

Olaf loves to dream of wonderful things. Write about your dreams on these pages.

Something I've always dreamed of doing

....

....

A place I dream of visiting

....

....

A person I dream of meeting

....

....

The last dream I remember having in my sleep

....

....

The best dream I've ever had

....

....

....

....

....

....

....

READY FOR ADVENTURE!

Olaf loves going on new adventures. Fill in these pages about your own trips and holidays.

My best ever adventure

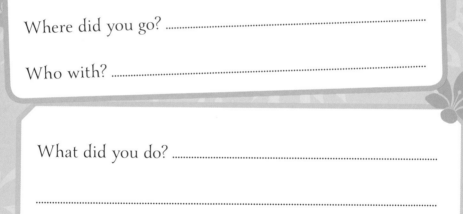

Where did you go? ....

Who with? ....

What did you do? ....

....

What was the best thing about it? ....

....

....

My next big adventure

Where are you going? ....

Who with? ....

What are you going to do? ....

....

What will be the best thing about it? ....

....

....

....

....

OLAF'S TOP FUN TIPS

This fun-loving snowman has some great advice for having a good time. Check it out!

Try new things

You never know if you're going to enjoy something until you try it.

TRUST YOUR FRIENDS

If they have an idea for a fun game or activity, give it a go!

Keep smiling!

Even when things seem hard, if you smile then people around you will feel like smiling, too.

BOUNCE BACK

When something goes wrong, put yourself back together and carry on.

Now write down some ideas for fun things you can do

1. ....

   ....

2. ....

   ....

3. ....

   ....

4. ....

   ....

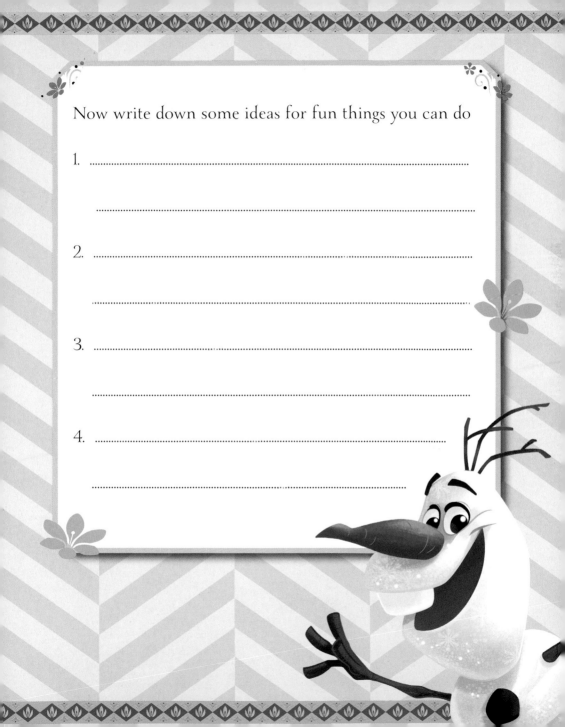

"I WISH ..."

Olaf's wishes are to experience summer and for his friends to be happy. What are yours?

I wish ....

....

because ....

....

I wish ....

....

because ....

....

I wish ....

....

because ....

....

I wish ....

....

because ....

....

DO YOU WANT TO BUILD A SNOWMAN?

Elsa made Olaf using magic, but you can draw a snowman or woman just using your pencil! Draw one here.

Fill in these fun facts
about your snowperson.

Name ....

He/she loves ....

....

He/she always says ....

....

His/her biggest dream is to

....

....

WHICH FROZEN FRIEND ARE YOU?

Circle your answers then check your results on the next page!

1. Which of these colours do you like the most?

    a) green
    b) blue
    c) yellow

2. Which season do you like the most?

    a) spring
    b) I don't mind
    c) summer

3. How would you most like to spend your day?

    a) walking in the forest
    b) making ice sculptures
    c) sunbathing on a beach

4. Which of these is your favourite?
   a) singing
   b) ice skating
   c) making jokes

5. Which of these are you most likely to say?
   a) "I can't wait!"
   b) "Let's think about it first."
   c) "I love heat!"

6. Which of these is closest to your own dream?
   a) to be surrounded by friends and family
   b) to be free to be yourself
   c) for it to be sunny all the time

7. Which of these best describes you?
   a) happy and excitable
   b) careful and graceful
   c) funny and loving

WHICH FROZEN FRIEND ARE YOU?

Add up your answers on the previous pages and read your results below.

RESULTS

Mostly a

You're Anna! You always look on the bright side and believe that everything will turn out okay. You love nature and flowers.

Mostly b

You're Elsa! You like to think things over before taking action. You are graceful, elegant and magical and you love playing in the snow.

Mostly c

You're Olaf! You like to be surrounded by friends and can always see the funny side of things. You're great at putting yourself back together after a fall and you love sunshine and making jokes.

WHAT'S YOUR FROZEN NAME?

For your **first name**, use your birth date. If the date has two numbers, add them together until you just have one.
e.g. 29th becomes 2 + 9 = 11, then 1 + 1 = 2

For your **middle name**, use your age

For your **last name**, use the number of letters in your real last name

First names

(BOYS)	(GIRLS)
1. Klaus	1. Annelise
2. Gunnar	2. Gerda
3. Rikard	3. Rae
4. Tomas	4. Thora
5. Bjorn	5. Anna
6. Olaf	6. Johanna
7. Hans	7. Susanna
8. Kristoff	8. Britta
9. Cornelis	9. Elsa
10. Henrik	10. Klara

Middle names

(BOYS)
3. Sled
4. Sven
5. Rudolf
6. Lars
7. Anders
8. Finn
9. Roald
10. Viktor
11. Iceman

(GIRLS)
3. Hilda
4. Sparkle
5. Magic
6. Vita
7. Snow
8. Wilhelmina
9. Christa
10. Astrid
11. Lake

Last names

2. Gunnarsson
3. Eriksson
4. Kingdom
5. Bergman
6. Lumi
7. Magiska
8. Rosenkrantz
9. Arendelle
10. Linna

Write your Frozen name here

....

....

....

PLAN YOUR OWN OLAF PARTY

Game: Pin the carrot on Olaf

1 With an adult's help, draw a big picture of Olaf on a large, plain piece of paper, but leave out his carrot nose. Now attach the picture to a wall at your party – make sure it's at a good height for your guests to reach Olaf's face.

2 Next, draw Olaf's carrot nose onto a separate piece of paper. Colour it orange and then cut it out. Add a piece of double-sided sticky tape to the back. Now find a scarf to use as a blindfold.

3 Each guest now takes a turn to wear the blindfold and try to 'pin the carrot on Olaf'. The person who pins it closest to where it's meant to go (on his nose) is the winner!

4 To keep track of where everyone puts the carrot, use a pencil to mark a little cross and put the person's initials next to it. That way, at the end of the game you can easily see who was closest.

Fancy dress

Ask your friends to dress as snowmen and women. They can use old white bed sheets, fluffy cotton wool and cardboard carrot noses. It'll be ice cool!

Party food

Give your guests snow and ice-themed food, like fluffy white marshmallows and melting Olaf cookies (see the recipe on the next page).

Party bags

When your party is over, give each of your guests a party bag to take home. You can fill it with sweets, treats and a piece of birthday cake.

RECIPE: MELTING SNOW COOKIES

Bake some scrummy cookies to serve at your Olaf party, or just to share with your friends and family.

What you'll need:

250g softened butter

140g caster sugar

1 egg yolk

2 teaspoons of vanilla extract

300g plain flour

350g of icing sugar

Sweets to decorate

How to make the cookies:

1. Ask an adult to preheat the oven to 180°C (fan oven 160°C, gas mark 4).

2. Mix together the butter and caster sugar in a large bowl.

3. Add the egg yolk, then the vanilla extract and mix again.

4. Sift in the flour and stir to mix it in. You might need to use your hands at the end to press the dough together.

5. Roll out the dough on a floured surface until it's about 1 cm thick.

6. Use a round cookie cutter to cut out your circle-shaped cookies.

7. Place your cookies on a greased baking tray and ask an adult to put them in the oven for 10 to 12 minutes, until they turn golden brown.

8. Remove the cookies from the oven and leave them to cool.

How to make the icing:

1. Mix the icing sugar with a little warm water. Mix until the icing is thick enough to stay on the back of a spoon.

2. Add a splodge of white icing to each cookie to look like melting snow.

3. Add some sweets to decorate.

DISCOVER YOUR FUTURE! ❄

Use this fun game to find out what your future holds.

1. First, write your own options on the blank lines in each category. Be as imaginative as you like!

2. Next, roll a die four times and write down the numbers you get. (If you get a 5 or 6, just roll again.)

3. The first number you rolled is your 'place to live', the second is your 'country', the third is your 'friend's name' and the last is your 'pet's name'. Now use your answers to complete the sentence!

Places to live

1. mansion

2. flat

3. shed

4. house

Countries

1.

2.

3.

4.

Friends' names

1. ....

2. ....

3. ....

4. ....

Funny pet names

1. ....

2. ....

3. ....

4. ....

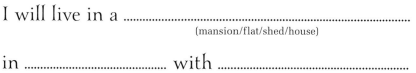

I will live in a ....
                        (mansion/flat/shed/house)

in .... with ....
       (country)   (friend's name)

We'll have a pet called .... !
                                    (pet's name)